A teacher's guide to
DESIGN & TECHNOLOGY AND THE HISTORIC ENVIRONMENT

Jonathan Barnes

Don

CONTENTS

David Walmsley

ABOUT THIS BOOK

Berney Arms Mill, Norfolk.

Hoover factory, west London.

Maiden Castle hillfort, Dorset.

Stott Park Bobbin Mill, Lake District.

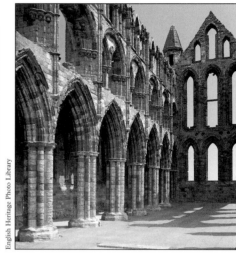

Whitby Abbey, North Yorkshire.

Look through the window closest to where you are sitting – is it a good or a poor view? What makes it attractive or boring? How have people made or changed it? What might improve it? Why is there a window there anyway? Without moving from your chair or wielding a single tool you have been involved in a design and technology activity; investigating aspects of a product, distinguishing between how it was made and how it was designed perhaps applying skills and knowledge from other subject areas such as history, art and mathematics.

This book:

■ explores the ways in which you can use any historic environment, from a school or housing estate to a castle or cathedral, to stimulate exciting design and technology assignments or to build up a fund of knowledge to be applied to otherwise unrelated projects

■ encourages teachers to get out of the classroom so that design and technology work can be placed in a real context

■ explains how teachers can use the historic sites in the care of English Heritage for more than just the predictable history field trip

■ argues that design and technology projects should be kept small and manageable unless teachers are able to devote many days to planning.

The National Curriculum in design and technology expects pupils to develop, plan and communicate ideas through designing and making as well as thinking about the made world. It involves the application of scientific and related knowledge to a problem; identifying the most appropriate tools and materials for the job; knowing how to use them safely and efficiently and finally producing a plan and/or product to solve the problem. Practical capability is needed, but the

subject has its own knowledge and understanding, and requires an awareness of alternatives and an evaluation process. The historic built environment is an excellent place to learn these aspects of design and technology because each building is a collection of the work of many designers and dozens of technological skills. Teachers and pupils should also be aware of the application of creative minds to the appearance of a final product. Design and technology may be taught alongside subjects like history, geography, maths and science which are more commonly the focus of a historic site visit. At its most well planned, design arising from the historic environment will leave pupils with a feeling that the designed world around them is worthy of closer attention.

This book will make reference to the constructed world of the past, details of which may now be found in museum collections as well as in buildings and landscapes.

WHY USE THE HISTORIC ENVIRONMENT?

An historic environment need not be a castle, monastery or country house – it could equally be the street nearest your school, the school itself, your local church, museum, shopping centre or public gardens. Whether your pupils are recording aspects of these places, proposing improvements, using parts of them as inspiration or planning an activity within them, they will be fulfilling some parts of the design and technology curriculum.

Throughout history design and technology skills have generally been applied in response to a need. These needs have often involved improving the quality of life but the solutions have not presented themselves out of the blue – they have arisen out of a mix of previous experience and creativity.

Look through your window again. However new the environment it is historic in some sense. How would you improve the view? Would you plant a tree? Paint a drainpipe? Place a piece of sculpture or demolish a wall? Sketch your idea of the improved view on a scrap of paper, or plan a better window frame to enclose it if you like it as it is. You have identified a need, planned a solution and moved some way towards making a product (especially if you felt inspired to make a model or ring the double glazing salesperson). Perhaps you are already evaluating or adapting your idea. Think how much more interesting this activity might have been if you were looking through an unfamiliar window onto an unusual scene.

English Heritage Photo Library

Pupils record measurements of the castle ramparts so that they can make an accurate scale model back in school.

It is the unfamiliarity of most historic environments that is perhaps their greatest strength. The unique-ness of these surround-ings can be harnessed to motivate both teachers and pupils towards more imaginative ideas. Many historic sites have the added benefit of being traffic free and enclosed but nevertheless safety must be considered in visit preparations and in the pupil/teacher ratio. They are also places where a variety of sub-ject perspectives can be taken and worked upon in various groups within a class during a single visit.

DETAIL AND SCALE

Working in a challenging and dif-ferent environment allows you to direct pupils to detail and the small scale. This is important because design and technology can be weakened when too much depends upon large scale theoretical projects such as design a theme park or construct a model of a proposed underground station. Since many pupils find difficulty in even gluing card together, this kind of assignment is almost bound to fail for all but the most able. Design a postcard based upon four contrasting doorways or take four digital photographs expressing four different moods of your local church in preparation for an advertising poster may be a more worthwhile exercise for novices.

Even to the television and video generation a well chosen historic

The view through a window can be greatly affected by the style of the frame.

English Heritage Photo Library

Well-planned activities led by teachers can add to pupils' understanding of the built environments of the past.

Church interiors may contain some of the finest examples in design and technology of their age.

site can be a stimulating and exciting experience without direction from a teacher. Given that our historic sites and museums are our most accessible repositories of the technologies of the past, structured and well-planned activities lead by a teacher can make the very most of natural inquisitiveness.

Your local parish church is often an obvious place to start, since the technologies used to build, furnish and decorate them were usually of a high order. Often these technologies have been frozen in time because of the special position of churches in our culture. Even modernisations have usually been done sympathetically and it is frequently possible visually to disassemble component parts of arches, windows, special furniture or decorations.

Whilst a church can be a valuable starting point for this approach to design and technology, do consider using your high street no matter how modern. The shopping street in any town displays a vast and varied collection of letter boxes, door knobs, window frames and lettering styles. Street furniture from sign posts to drain covers have all been through a rigorous design process. Local councils or individuals may have employed the best designers and crafts people available. From this viewpoint every collection of shops, houses or lamp posts can be seen as a pattern book of designs and practical solutions. The older the building the more signs there may be of a succession of answers to the same problem — think of an old door with the scars of previous locks and catches giving evidence of past technologies.

The great joy of using the historic environment for a design and technology assignment is that you do not need to know a great deal about history. Use castles, cathedrals, warehouses and woollen mills but do not feel guilty if you do not know exactly when they were built or who slept in them. A basic knowledge of the sequence of architectural styles would allow for a valuable extra dimension in design and technology work but a great deal can still be obtained from using historic environments simply as the complex products of past design skill and technological expertise.

Furnished houses provide further opportunities for design and technology.

5

CHOOSING AN ASSIGNMENT

Most successful technological developments have sprung from a need. Basic needs for food, shelter, security, meaning and contact have never changed and have provided the motivation for most major human achievements. Modern priorities of sustainable economic growth, mass housing, international co-operation, rapid communication and conservation stem from the same needs which troubled the builders of Roman towns. Whilst needs may not alter, the means to supply them change with time, culture, economy and developments in design and technology itself. Your pupils should be aware that needs have been supplied by every technological advance. Their own work will be more satisfying if it is seen as the result of some demand – even the need for clearer signposts to the local beauty spot.

PREPARATION

It is vital of course that teachers make a preliminary visit to the historic environment they intend to use as the starting point for a design and technology activity. You will need to observe, discuss, photograph and draw the aspects of the environment you wish your pupils to use. Look for:

■ things which move

■ things which have a modern equivalent

■ areas where unusual materials have been used

■ joins between materials or components

■ dramatic views

■ fine detail.

During the preliminary visit it is a good idea to draw and make notes on some of the details you observe.

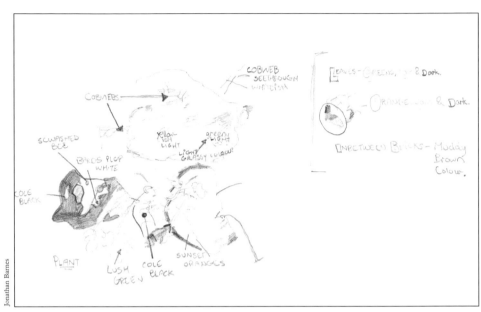
Encourage pupils to make notes on their drawings.

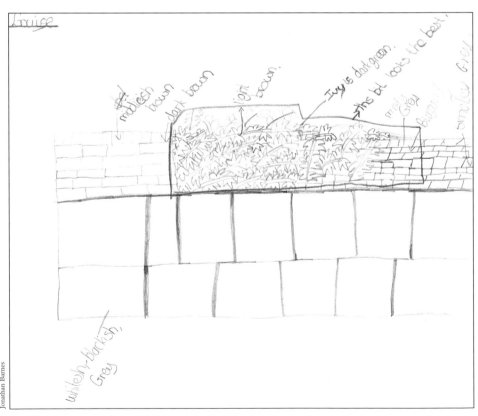
Avoid shading and take a full frontal view which reduces the problems of perspective.

Teachers frequently encourage pupils to draw as an efficient way of collecting evidence and focusing the mind. The same is true for adults. The function of drawing in this context is not the production of works of art but the recording of information: how the product has been made, how it moves and how it might be disassembled. A good assignment often becomes clear during such a drawing activity.

When on site your pupils should be encouraged to make frequent annotated sketches of small details:

how something moves

colour

 materials

construction techniques

how different parts are joined

evidence of change.

Eighteenth-century fire insurance plate inspired this design and make assignment.

CONSERVATION

Pupils may note that parts of buildings, streets or even landscapes show signs of wear, damage and decay. They may well be lead on to make a careful sketch of a small section of weathered wall or use a plan to plot the signs of deterioration in an historic building. Pupils will become more aware of conservation issues if they see and fully appreciate the effects of a lack of conservation.

Try some of the following class activities using the school grounds or the streets near your school:

make a drawing of the roofscape of the street emphasizing television aerials, satellite dishes, burglar alarm boxes, wires, flues and chimneys. Use the drawings back at school to generate a discussion on the environmental intrusion of such features and methods of minimising it. This might lead on to a roofscape design for a school mural or scenery for the school play

select several key features from an attractive building in your area, photograph them individually. Back at school, use the cut out or sketched features to improve a photograph or drawing of an unattractive local building. This could be done using photomontage, by careful drawing or perhaps using screen printing techniques

■ make a photographic record of a multi-storey car park, tower block or factory near you. Consider softening harsh external features by adding cladding, vegetation, colour, lighting or other disguises. Make a before and after catalogue of the most effectively improved buildings

■ walk along your local high street looking at shop fascias and the floors above street level. Pupils may make detailed drawings of individual shops to focus this activity. Back at school decide which building as a whole is most appealing. Discuss why this is.

How might you use these decorative elements on other products?

Devise ways of harmonising unsympathetic shop fronts with their upper floors

■ make a collection of drawings of door knockers, letter boxes, latches, fan lights or house number lettering styles. This collection and the class evaluation which follows could lead on to a design and make assignment on the same theme.

Some shop fronts do not make concessions to the history of the building.

Should we leave old barns as monuments to the past or adapt them to modern uses?

CONVERSIONS AND ADDITIONS

We all know of the double glazing, garage extensions, conservatories and loft conversions which have ruined the appearance of houses we like. English Heritage mounted a campaign to draw attention to some of the excesses of barn conversion schemes. These adaptations to modern life are not a new feature of the built environment – modernisations, conversions and quite unsympathetic additions have occurred throughout history. None the less we probably value our historic environment more today than ever and most would agree that it is important to preserve the best of it.

Since adaptation and modernisation will always be part of our relationship with buildings, it is important that pupils are taught a sensitivity to them and the landscapes in which they stand. Today we are becoming increasingly conscious of the environmental impact of such changes.

Base any of the following design activities on historic buildings near you:

■ design a dog kennel or nesting box in the style of your local town hall, country house or factory. Identify those features of the building which could be applied at a smaller scale to the miniature home

■ design and make models for the conversion of a redundant building in your area. Consider transforming it into a sports or community centre. First of all pupils will need to be familiar with the building – its dimensions, limitations and position. Remind pupils at the outset that the essential character and detail of the building will need to be maintained

■ plan a discrete addition to your nearest castle or ecclesiastical ruin – maybe a visitor centre or gift shop. Start with a careful survey of the building materials, styles of architecture methods of construction and forms of decoration. Draw profiles from different angles of approach. Back at school sketch ideas, discuss and agree upon a scheme which could then be made to scale and attached to a simple model of the existing monument.

Design a new extension for an abbey ruin perhaps to house a cafe or new exhibition.

CASE STUDY: THE TANNERY PROJECT

Pupils at a primary school chose the industrial site of a tannery just behind their school for a re-development project which centred upon ideas of conservation and the sympathetic realisation of a community's needs. The project was to be inter-disciplinary and to last a term. The tannery, which included several listed industrial buildings of the eighteenth and nineteenth centuries, was still working but the owners were hoping to resite out of town on an industrial estate.

From the outset careful pre-paration was needed by teachers because a decision had been taken to make sure that pupils worked with professionals – architects, planners, builders and local authority officials. Their con-tribution had to be thoroughly thought out, as did the intro-duction of the knowledge and skills they would need to fulfil the assignment in their groups of six or seven.

The groups were each given the following brief

to find out:

what the community thinks of the tannery at present

what the community feels it needs on the site if it is re-developed

what uses the site has had in the past.

to record:

findings of questionnaires on public opinion

present appearance of the site and its locality

information about the history of the site.

to decide:

which uses are compatible with the area

how the listed buildings can be used

what projects will be in the groups plan.

to draw:

plans of group proposals

favourite details

elevations of listed buildings and key build-ings in the locality.

to map:

details of proposals

historical findings.

to construct:

models of proposals

an exhibition of all findings and activities.

Jonathan Barnes

Model-making in teams develops important social and work skills.

At each stage of the brief professionals were brought in to teach basic skills and principles at an appropriate level. They had previously contributed to staff development days where they taught teachers the requisite skills.

After surveys of the site, questionnaires and detailed analysis of the site pupils decided on a mixed development of houses, small local shops, a craft centre and a hotel. They realised that parking and access had to be carefully considered when they worked with a city planning officer. A conservation architect from English Heritage told them what they could and could not do with the listed buildings and drew their attention to details of building materials and scale which needed to be considered in the proposed new buildings.

The final exhibition of group proposals was a great success with all visitors. Parents and professionals outside education were surprised at the high quality of the pupils' work and the pupils themselves were very proud of their propositions. Teachers could instantly see how much high quality geography, history, maths, science, art and English was involved in the project.

Teachers at the school were relieved to find in the project evaluation that they had covered all targets they would have set in a more formal term's work. Visitors to the exhibition noted how highly motivated the pupils were and how the skills they had learned in one area of the brief had been transferred to other areas. Indeed teachers commented for some time afterwards that the pupils were using their new found abilities in a great variety of other contexts.

GAMES AND SOUVENIRS

The gift shops of most historic sites provide a very important source of income and for some pupils the most memorable part of a visit. Whilst it is relatively easy to buy 'ye olde English toffee' or pot-pourri at any of them it is some-times difficult to find unique souvenirs which only arise from that monument. Museums have found, however, that reproductions of their more famous artefacts are both a popular purchase and fairly inexpensive to produce. Whilst it would not be good economic sense to arrange for scale models of each historic building in the area, there is a case for a school working with the nearest monument to produce real, saleable and unique souvenirs. For example:

■ draw three different kinds of building material by looking through a viewfinder at three contrasting areas of wall in a chosen building. Drawings should be very detailed and include colour notes. Back at school the most satisfying drawing could become the basis of a design applied to a scarf, t-shirt, handkerchief or teatowel. Make the prototype on paper, modify and then transfer the design to an appropriate material, cotton calico or linen. This activity could also be achieved using designs from flooring

■ make outline drawings of different profiles of a building or historic area. Concentrate on view points where one layer of building overlaps with another. Back at school, design and make a toast or letter rack by using three or four differ-ent profiles placed one in front of the other. This idea is best made from air-drying clay slabs as in the diagram above

■ use a polaroid camera to capture twelve unusual views of a monument. Choose one as the subject for a postcard or jigsaw

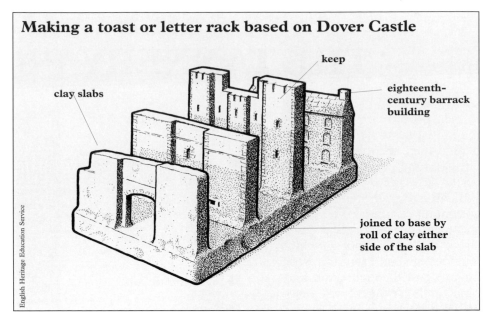

Making a toast or letter rack based on Dover Castle

clay slabs

keep

eighteenth-century barrack building

joined to base by roll of clay either side of the slab

English Heritage Education Service

puzzle. Close-ups of architectural details, sections of lichen encrusted wall or carpet designs could be used. The collected results from several groups could be evaluated and three or four views produced commercially – perhaps for the school Christmas card.

English Heritage Photo Library

English Heritage Photo Library

David Walmsley

Designs inspired by ancient walling can be applied to fabric for a variety of purposes.

MEALS

The planning and preparation of a Roman, medieval or Victorian meal can bring together a number of important skills whilst making many good historical points.

A visit to an historic site such as a monastery or a large house can be used to investigate the systems required to feed a large household and the ceremonies or traditions which surrounded the production of a meal. During a visit, look for the places where food might have been kept cool, dry and clean. Attempt to discover where it was cooked and eaten. It needs to be stressed that the physical needs and limitations of human beings have changed little over the centuries. For example, any distance between kitchen and dining-room presented problems in the past as it would today. How did they keep food warm? If conditions in a

Even in medieval ruins there are design clues to point towards its use as a kitchen.

Mosaic floor in the dining-room at Lullingstone Roman Villa.

room feel cramped, damp and cold to us then pupils could be asked to consider if this would also be true for people of the past.

FOOD IN A MEDIEVAL BUILDING

Where was food stored?

■ Look for low, dark, dry accessible spaces with lots of room but little evidence of domestic use, for example no fireplaces

■ Look for smaller lockable spaces for storing more precious foods such as salt, sugar and spices.

Where was food prepared?

■ Locate the largest fireplace, smoke vents, gullies or upturned tiles in the floor

■ Look at the proximity to the main eating room and the degree of finish which expresses the importance of the function of cooking.

How was the food taken from kitchen to dining room?

■ Look for corridors, ceremonial or service entrances, dumb waiters, back stairs and passageways behind screens in the main eating room.

Where was the food eaten?

■ Find a large domestic room with a high degree of decoration, perhaps a raised dais at one end

■ Look for access to private chambers after a meal.

What happened to waste?

■ Look for chutes and gullies from the kitchen area, rubbish pits, latrine shafts, garderobes and closets.

PRESERVING OUR HERITAGE

In these days of theme parks and reconstructions the question may be asked – why preserve historic buildings and artefacts at all? Many answers could be given but most depend to an extent upon a recognition that the historic environment is an inheritance – something we can all share and enjoy but something we also have a responsibility for. Historic buildings of every age hold examples of every kind of technological advance just as the rain forests maintain a huge variation of different life forms. Preserving both natural and historic environments can be seen as a means of maintaining a kind of bank of genes or technologies for use some time in the future. There is however too much potential in both kinds of environment just to keep them away from public view – most people view them as beautiful in some way and want to see and understand them.

If pupils are to regard the historic environment as both beautiful and theirs, they need to be educated to have a sensitivity towards it. Many of the activities in this book will help develop this sensitivity.

CASE STUDY: HERITAGE CITIZENSHIP

To foster a concern for the historic environment whilst developing social and literacy skills, Year 5 and 6 pupils investigated the most popular historic building within a chosen locality – their local high street. As part of their preparation for the project, pupils investigated old maps, directories and photographs gathering as much information as they could find. They discussed the meanings of new words such as restoration, conservation, and preservation. They also practised annotated sketching using the school buildings.

A straw poll was taken within the school as to the most popular historic building in the high street. When making their choice, pupils were not allowed to consider the function of the building. This was then compared with the findings of a similar poll taken in the high street where pupils interviewed members of the local community. On the questionnaire the following questions were asked:

what is your favourite building in the area?

why do you like it?

what would you feel if it were demolished?

how could it be improved?

The high street had many historic buildings so it was thought advisable to ask people to select from a given list.

Having compared the two straw polls, pupils identified the most popular historic building. Pupils were set the task to answer three questions:

does it need to be preserved?

does it need restoration?

does it need modernisation?

They visited the building to undertake a detailed survey of its features, state of repair and importance within the community. They made detailed notes and sketches of what the building was made of. Some pupils took photographs for use back in school. They also noted any damaged features – what they were and where they were located. This developed into more formal proposals for restoration work.

In school, pupils also made a scale model of the building, wrote detailed illustrated survey reports on the condition of the building and designed posters to campaign for its full restoration. The work developed into an investigation into how the needs of a particular historic building could be fulfilled. The local authority conservation officer was invited into school to talk to the pupils and answer their questions.

Working within the constraints of a real building avoided the formless and unrealistic results of the more usual design activity. The most obvious outcome for the pupils undertaking this project was a massive rise in sensitivity to other conservation issues related to the built environment near their school. They were given opportunites to express their personal opinions on a building in their own community and present their findings in many different forms including much design and technology. As well as engaging the enthusiasm of the pupils, the project also developed a sense of responsibility towards the buildings in their community.

By studying the conservation issues of a local historic building, pupils can develop a sense of responsibility towards buildings in their community.

Identifying and sketching the state of repair of building featues can raise conservation questions.

To relate to the historic environment, pupils need to have been physically involved with it.

DESIGNING SKILLS

DEVELOPING AWARENESS

An understanding of the aesthetic properties of a building can be an important product of a visit to an historic environment. Consider, for example, the elements which have came together in a nineteenth-century railway station – the original brackets, impressive doorways, moulded ironwork, decorative brickwork and fretwork canopy. Look for evidence of modern alterations – changes to the ticket office, waiting room, toilets or buffet. Have the modernisations been done in sympathy with the original design or do they stand out as obvious, even jarring? What do these observations suggest about the relationship between design and economics, business and aesthetics?

Since the historic environment can be said to be generally valued and often aesthetically pleasing it may be appropriate to use it to introduce pupils to some aesthetic considerations. Why does one building seen to harmonise with its surroundings whereas another looks out of place? Why do some replacement windows look so obvious? Before embarking on a major design and technology project based around field work,

David Walmsley

Recent cleaning and restoration have sometimes drawn greater attention to design features.

one or more of the following activities may be of use in developing an aesthetic awareness:

■ walk your pupils up and down a street of terraced houses near the school. Ask them to decide which front doors or windows are most likely to be the original ones. They could draw or photograph these original features and discuss what design characteristics link them to the rest of the house. Are there motifs which are repeated elsewhere in the house? Is the same decorative moulding

Suzanne Spicer

Are modernisations of railway stations in sympathy with their original design?

Suzanne Spicer

Which features are original? How can you tell?

used in both door and window frames? Are the panels of glass in the window and door of similar proportion? Identify a replacement door which was not designed with the houses and discuss which parts give it away

■ prepare a drawing of a well known older building near you – perhaps the church, town hall or school buildings. In your drawing (or doctored photograph) deliberately leave out crucial windows or doors. Prepare a number of drawings of alternative features to fill the gap in various styles. Allow a group to experiment with the replacement windows or doors and write the reasons for their eventual choice

■ alter a photograph or drawing of a well-known and symmetrical historic monument by removing some projections – chimney stacks, towers, turrets, spires or cupolas. Photocopy the altered picture and ask groups or individuals to complete the building in a balanced and harmonious way, by drawing onto the photocopy.

Most historic environments are complex systems – many have evolved over time and all are difficult to understand fully at first sight. Drawing a simple elevation or preparing even the most elementary plan is an effective way to help pupils come to terms with a complicated site. It is also a very successful way of allowing time for reflection and developing a crucial communication skill in design and technology. Such drawings can be used for reference in model making or to aid the design of artefacts.

English Heritage Education Service

Fill in the missing details from Audley End House.

CASE STUDY: RECONSTRUCTING A RUINED BUILDING

Year 8 pupils studying Medieval Realms in history combined with the design and technology department to make a reconstruction model of part of St Augustine's Abbey in Canterbury. The project took eight hours in total.

During a general visit, the history teacher led investigations into the historical development of the site. The pupils then made a second visit in which they were set to work by the design and technology teacher. She asked one group to measure and record the dimensions of the floor plan of St Pancras' chapel. Another group had to measure the height of existing walls and work out which was most representative of the actual height of the original building. A third group recorded details of the construction methods and materials used in walling. The last group looked at the dimensions, style and building techniques of window and door openings.

St Augustine's Abbey, Canterbury.

Each group spent a double lesson back at school putting their findings in an appropriate form and then made a presentation of their findings to the others. Using the combined information from all the groups, the pupils began to make a scaled reconstruction of the ruined chapel. Technology staff taught simple model-making skills and each of the four groups made their own version of the chapel of St Pancras as it was in 1066. Evaluation was undertaken by the groups themselves. Since each individual had been involved in making a similar model, all knew the brief and its difficulties and everyone had constructive suggestions as to how to improve their own and others' designs.

Pupils were tasked with calculating the height of the original building.

A group investigated the dimensions, style and building techniques of windows and doorways.

LOOKING FOR DETAIL

Pupils benefit from being directed to a small detail rather than a whole building or street. Investigating how different materials (wood and stone, metal and glass, bricks and mortar) have been joined in a medieval house can be much more engaging then a dry lecture on the history of the building. Simply indicating interesting things is not riveting for most pupils, so construct a mini project which focuses on small detail. This can be a much more rewarding activity, wit and imagination can be given full rein – the more unusual the ideas the more the pupils will be interested.

Imagine if medieval engineers had attempted to design an angle-poise table lamp using medieval technologies and perceptions, what might it have looked like? How would the Normans have constructed an automatic toaster? Such a line of thought could be used to make unusual starting points for the design of everyday domestic items. For example:

■ redesign a bus shelter or telephone box to make it harmonise with a historically sensitive area

■ look at street lights in your neighbourhood and design a table lamp using features collected from different lamp posts

■ plan and make in card a pair of novelty spectacles using classical, medieval or Victorian features

■ design and make a pencil box which uses the mechanisms and decorative features of a Victorian sash window

■ make ceramic chess pieces based on the individual upstanding features of a complex building like a castle or mansion

■ construct a knitting pattern using either a design from an historic country house, garden or the symmetrical room plan of a Palladian mansion

■ make a book cover with working hinges, bolts and other door furniture like a church or a castle door

■ use medieval ways of joining two pieces of wood to suggest ideas for buttons or brooches

■ scale down two church or castle towers to make them into practical salt and pepper pots. Any domes near you could be removed and their bases become the basis of an egg cup

■ make some stained-glass earrings based on a window near you

■ produce signposts which fit the environment in which they are to be placed

■ design a logo for your town or local historic monument using some of the more surprising features of the building.

If a Norman designer had thought of an eggcup, would it have looked liked this?

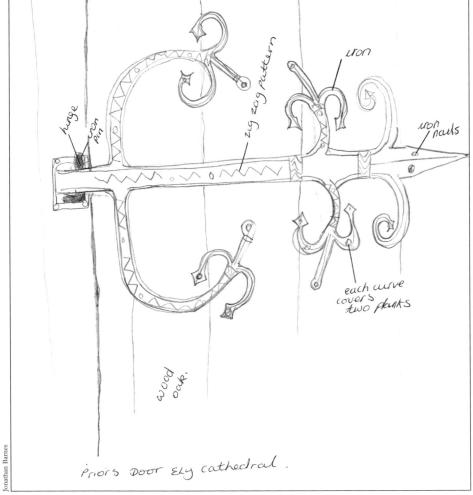

zig zag pattern

iron

hinge

iron pin

iron nails

each curve covers two planks

wood oak.

Priors Door Ely cathedral.

Always look for detail.

Castle towers can form the basis of a pepperpot design.

OBJECTS

The well planned use of objects in a classroom setting can be used to build upon design and technology fieldwork. Building materials, and examples of the hinges brackets, drain covers, plugs, handles or hooks used in modern building will encourage your pupils to consider the small details of the design solutions of others before embarking on their own.

Use some of these ideas to help generate or enrich design and technology projects:

■ look for imported materials in a museum collection of Victorian artefacts. Discover what attributes made foreign materials like tortoise shell, ostrich feathers, mahogany or ivory popular. Suggest modern

Observational drawing of an object encourages pupils to look for details in design.

equivalents for these materials and compare their properties

■ make the unusual shapes and textures of architectural hardware (pipes, grilles, fixings, door

and window furniture) the subject of fabric design

■ build an exhibition of local building materials and techniques. Design the labels, decide which exhibits should be placed with each other, plan the layout and route around the exhibition and advertise it with posters and catalogues.

Each object in this room has been through a design process.

CASE STUDY: DESIGN A TIE

A group of Year 5 pupils in a country school in Suffolk were set the assignment of designing a tie on the theme of walls.

Just outside the school there were a number of flint, brick and sandstone walls and plenty of wooden garden fences. Pupils were asked to identify a place where two materials were placed next to each other. They were to make a very detailed drawing using a view finder to cut out extraneous features. The area of wall they had to draw had to be no more than 30cms by 30cms. They were also asked to make careful colour notes on their drawings. Each pupil had to draw a different area of the wall.

Back in school, pupils selected the most satisfying part of their drawing and placed a card frame around it. This framed area was to be the repeated pattern used on the tie design. The pupils then drew a prototype design onto a prepared tie template made of paper.

After evaluating each others' work and adapting some of their designs, the pupils drew their proposals onto cloth templates with special coloured pencils. Their designs were worn home.

Here pupils were encouraged to look objectively at the historic environment and concentrate on detail – a section of a wall. Their reference drawings could also have been developed into designs for tablecoths, wallpaper, fabric and handkerchiefs using different techniques such as lino or screen printing.

The raw material for a design project.

Small details of large buildings can be as fascinating as the more monumental aspects.

THINKING ABOUT PROBLEMS

How have tall walls, sometimes a thousand years old, remained upright? How can you provide lots of natural light whilst needing strong walls to support a heavy roof? How did they build bridges before reinforced concrete? These and similar technological problems were solved in a huge variety of ingenious ways in the past and still test the minds of our engineers and designers today.

The principles of keeping verticals vertical are the same for cardboard as they are for fences or massive masonry.

For beginners, perhaps the best illustration of the range of solutions to a problem is that of spanning the space between two uprights – from Stonehenge, through Roman and Gothic arches or brick lintels to the simple steel framed buildings of our age. Pupils may be set the task of building up a chronological set of illustrations and then move on to perform a

Spanning a gap is a common design and technology problem.

The first cast-iron bridge was constructed using techniques of timber construction.

task in which their findings could be put into practice. Perhaps the popular build a 'bridge out of spaghetti project' would be more meaningful if it were placed after such a study of historic solutions.

INSIDE INFORMATION

The historic environment includes the interiors of buildings and their furnishings. These present us with another dimension of technological problems and solutions. How did people stop draughts in vast open halls? What did they do to soften the cold harshness of huge empty walls? How did people build chairs before tubular steel and moulded plastic? Each element of an interior can become the starting point for design either as an example of an old solution or as a new inspiration.

Try some of the following design assignments:

■ make a carpet design from drawings of a pattern of floor-boards or quarry tiles

■ create a tessellating floor tile based upon a carpet design from a stately home. Use rotational symmetry to develop the pattern further

■ design and make a set of ceramic tea bowls decorated with patterns copied from a porcelain collection

■ draw the carved capitals of Romanesque or Gothic columns and use them to plan and make a large fruit bowl from clay

■ make plans for the conversion of a Victorian country house

kitchen into a profitable tea room

■ screen print your own wall paper based upon ecclesiastical furnishings or a pattern found on a piece of eighteenth-century furniture

■ make a hanging plant pot with gargoyles around the bottom for excess water to drip through.

Make a mental list of the designed features in this interior.

CASE STUDY: A CATHEDRAL VISIT

A Year 9 class from Lincoln was taken on a two hour design and technology visit to their local cathedral. The trip was designed to expose them to a range of past solutions to the problem of accommodating large numbers of people.

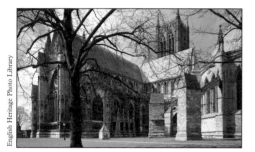

Lincoln Cathedral was used to explore spatial design.

Problem-solving assignments can also be extended to the Bishop's Palace. How many servants were there? How many guests could the Bishop entertain in the great hall?

Before the visit pupils listed the needs which had to be addressed in a cathedral building – a covered open space big enough for a thousand to see what was going on at the front, a large number of east facing altars for many priests to celebrate mass, plenty of space for ceremonies and processions, separation between priest and people, grand and inspiring in appearance, strong enough to last for ever, light enough to see without electric light.

Need	Solution
A symbolic shape	
Visible from afar	
Large open space	
Lots of east facing altars	
Space for processions	
Grand for great occasions	
Inspiring to look at	
Strength to last centuries	
As much light as possible	
Hearing the priest	
Separation for priest and people	
Able to teach the illiterate	

During the visit groups were asked to list the ways these needs had been met on the table shown above.

Other groups were given specific tasks to disassemble aspects of the cathedral, the great east window, one of the columns, a pointed arch, a flying buttress and a metal screen. These were drawn in exploded form, previously explained and practised in school.

After collecting their evidence, pupils were set the task of making a poster showing cathedral technology based around a commercial cut-away drawing of the cathedral.

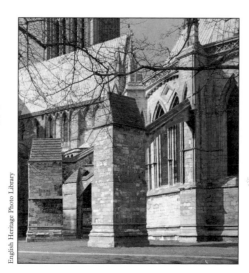

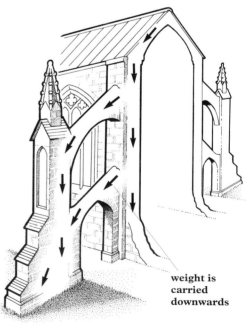

weight is carried downwards

Flying buttresses.

MAKING SKILLS

The earlier part of this book has been very much to do with planning assignments, collecting information and thinking about design. Such things as reference and working drawings, sketch designs and prototypes are very much part of the design process but the product itself uses more technological skills. Many of the ideas so far have been two-dimensional and preparatory, but the following suggestions involve working in three dimensions and perhaps more familiar design and technology territory.

MATERIALS OLD AND NEW

If we look around any modern built environment we see the impact of new materials like plastics, alloys, sheet glass, reinforced concrete and made fibres. Technology is as much a product of materials as it is of ideas. Modern materials have made modern technology possible. Pupils do not find it difficult to imagine life without these materials especially when given a visual or even manual aid. Ask a group to devise ways of moving a few litres of water across the playground without using glass, metal or plastic and they would rapidly begin to come up with answers and materials

The use of modern materials can be seen all around us.

from other times and other cultures.

Each material has its own particular qualities, these include appearance, weight, availability and a host of other attributes which make them either appropriate or not for a particular role. Use a matrix like the one below to help your pupils consider the crucial part materials play in the final appearance of a product.

Choosing appropriate materials for working with back at school is an important part of design and technology. Your pupils will need an opportunity to experiment with ways of joining these materials before they embark upon an actual project. Many good ideas have been spoiled by the use of inappropriate materials or the lack of basic making skills. Sometimes unusual or accidental choices of material may be quite exciting and lead to new design possibilities but the techniques of cutting, joining and strengthening need to be taught and not left to chance. A number of artists and designers

Using inappropriate materials in design and technology is not necessarily a twentieth-century conceit.

have made a speciality of using the wrong materials and using some of their more outlandish ideas is a useful means of teaching fundamental making skills. Try some of these ideas:

■ pasta jewellery based on an Egyptian collection

■ knitted crockery starting from a Wedgewood exhibition

■ grass furniture arising from a prehistoric earthwork

■ furniture inspired by waste materials on a building site

■ megalithic earrings stimulated by a visit to some standing stones

■ a Napoleonic 'tie pin' using a bolt seen in a nineteenth-century fortress as a starting point

■ sculptures which look like weathered stones.

THINKING ABOUT MATERIALS

	ITEM 1	CHARACTERISTIC	ITEM 2	CHARACTERISTIC	ITEM 3	CHARACTERISTIC
Name of item	tea cup	small liquid container with handle				
Main material	china	non-absorbent				
Other materials	glaze	colourful				
Joined by	slip	strong				
I liked item ..... best because						

Making movement in school technology requires a clear understanding of a few simple principles.

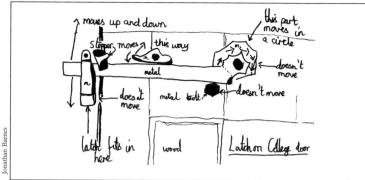

Simple mechanisms can be sketched on site and used in school to inspire models or inventions.

MAKING MOVEMENT

Before the nineteenth century most movement in the design of artefacts and buildings was based upon simple principles – levers, hinges, counterbalance, pullies and gears. A visit which concentrated on motion would direct pupils' attention to more unusual aspects of the historic environment. Mills, treadmills, mines and other industrial sites abound in examples of such movement but do not forget doors, folding furniture, casement windows, church bells, clocks and drawbridges. Whether in a factory or museum, examples of how things were made to move can be sketched or photographed and used back at school to inspire moving toys, models or inventions.

A visit to a watermill or windmill will supply memorable examples of simple mechanisms. Such a visit can be taken further by groups of any age and result in the construction of models which not only use elementary mechanical components but are also powered by renewable resources like wind and water. Since these ancient sources of power are undergoing a modern revival, pupils can also be given the chance to see and understand the technological origins of present day wind farms, wave power and hydro-electric turbines.

In the follow up from an historic site visit, consider the following suggestions:

■ make a 'pop up' model of two overlapping sections of an historic building or interior

■ construct a moving drawbridge based on the cantilever principle or a windlass

■ make a turning figure on a wheel based on the cogs from wooden mill machinery

■ build a jointed model of a knight in armour

■ copying old mechanisms with modern materials such as technic-lego can even be done on site so that a full grasp of the workings of these massive machines can be demonstrated. The same can be done with steam engines, church bells or mechanical clocks where the successful construction of a working model is a simple means of assessment.

Windmills use mechanisms that can be used to introduce pupils to the technology of movement.

KEY	A	Buck
	B	Post
	C	Fantail or Fly
	D	Fan Carriage
	E	Whip
	F	Vanes
	G	Windshaft
	H	Stock
	J	Clamps
	K	Spider
	L	Striking Chain
	M	Cross Trees
	N	Quarter Bars
	O	Sheers or Shutter Trees
	P	Crown Tree
	Q	Wears
	R	Bridge Tree
	S	Runner Stone
	T	Bed Stone
	U	Governer
	V	Meal Spout
	W	Horse
	Ww	Brake Wheel
	X	Wallower
	Xx	Stone Nut
	Y	Spindle Beam
	Z	Sack Hoist

CASE STUDY: MAKING A DRAWBRIDGE

A windlass drawbridge.

A cantilever drawbridge.

Pupils on a visit to Dover Castle were struck by the different types of drawbridge they saw. Two had been operated by using a wooden platform controlled by a see-saw action with heavy weights on the defenders' side. When additional pressure was put on the weighted end of the drawbridge it simply flipped up preventing intruders. Another part of the castle had a drawbridge which had once been hung on massive chains which were wound up on giant windlasses in the event of an attack. A more ingenious nineteenth-century version operated when a heavy, suspended door was released from above the drawbridge. The massive weight of the door was enough to pull up the drawbridge which was attached by chains to its lower end.

Pupils were set the task of making their own versions of the drawbridges when they returned to school. To accomplish this, individual groups investigated one drawbridge, sketching it and noting what materials were used and how they thought the mechanism worked. Each group also took a photographic record to be used as reference when working back in school.

In school each group used the information gathered on-site and began to make a model showing how their drawbridge worked. Simple model-making skills had been taught before embarking on the project and pupils were also familiar with using technic-lego. On completing their model, each group was asked to evaluate their mechanism and to make suggestions on how the design could be improved.

To extend and develop this project with older pupils, groups were asked to design their own modern drawbridge showing what materials they would use and how their mechanism would work. They had to make and test their own design. These were then compared to the designs found at Dover Castle.

Dover Castle.

MANUFACTURE AND MARKETING

Most making will need to happen back at school, or in an education centre, but the links with the historic environment need not be broken. Sketches and photographs have been mentioned many times and should always be available during the production of an artefact. Cameras and video can also be used. In the school library or using CD-ROM or the Internet, pupils could find other examples of similar structures or systems, research alternative answers to the problem, or study the solutions of other cultures. Thus making will be in the context of something bigger than the classroom.

Making should also take other important factors into account – the competent construction of the product and especially its final appearance. The aesthetic sensitivity gained from other subjects and through observation of historic environments can be used in the making of new ones. This applies as much to the accurate joining and combination of materials as to the finishing techniques applied to products. If the product is to utilize the special patina of an old object for example, then the means of achieving this effect will need to be experimented with. Pupils from Key Stage 2 onwards should also be aware of the preferences of consumers when deciding upon the presentation of their product.

Making things inspired by a visit to an historic site will of course require a knowledge of materials and techniques which can only be gained by previous experience. Measuring, marking out, cutting, shaping, joining slabs of clay, sections of card or making a wooden frame must be taught and can only really be learned by doing. Certain short cuts and hints can be useful in fulfilling some of the ideas presented in this book.

If the products are to be sold then important decisions need to be made. What packaging would best display the product and also most effectively communicate the relationship of the product with the historic site which inspired it? What market research needs to be

Using video and video stills

Video and video stills can be used in the historic environment to record information to be worked on back in school but they can also play a more integral role in a project. For example:

■ use a video camera to record interviews with a number of different people who work in an historic building. The viewpoints of managers, cleaners, custodians and conservationists may differ widely and help pupils appreciate the complex considerations which have to be made before making decisions affecting the historic environment. Create a video presentation which summarises different views on the same place

■ make a video which promotes an under-used historic environment in the vicinity of the school. Concentrate on the unique aspects, unusual view points and the importance of the monument to the history and present environment need of the place. After identifying the place

to be promoted, pupils will be involved in a number of serious decisions about which aspects to concentrate upon and which to gloss over. The video could be shown to parents or other special interest groups and perhaps even lead to the rediscovery of a lost, local gem

■ video footage or still images can successfully be used to plot the progress of a technology idea. Start with the preparation exercises and go in to cover the most valuable parts of a site visit. Trace the development of the product from planning to production and sale. The making of a video like this makes evaluation easy and is an invaluable method of communicating the good work of the school to parents and governors

■ make a 'Power point' presentation of examples of doors, letter boxes, lamp posts or door knockers from the streets around the school.

Video is a useful method of recording but it can also play a key role in technology work.

done? How will people of other cultures feel about it? Has the full social or environmental impact of

any proposed products been considered?

Making clay joints

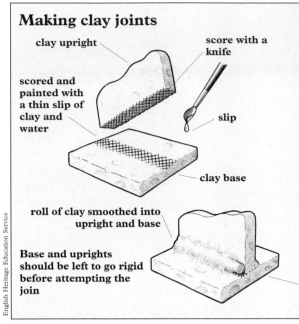

clay upright

score with a knife

scored and painted with a thin slip of clay and water

slip

clay base

roll of clay smoothed into upright and base

Base and uprights should be left to go rigid before attempting the join

Joining clay

Roll clay into slabs about 1cm thick using a rolling pin. Cut required shapes with a knife. Position the parts which are to be joined and mark the place where the join will occur. Score the edges of the two pieces to be joined. Mix a paste, called slip, from clay and water. Apply the paste to the place to be joined. Position the two pieces. Secure either side with two rolls of clay. Mash the clay rolls to hide the join and smooth the joined parts.

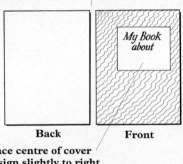

scoring helps the two parts to bond

Making cogs and wheels

Cut strips of thin dowel into sixteen sections. Take a card circle and mark sixteen equal points around it by bisecting the circle eight times. Glue dowel sections to the sixteen points. Cover with second card circle. Make smaller or larger cogs to fit with the first.

Making books

Place sticky fabric spine on table sticky side up. Place prepared back and front covers, face down, onto sticky spine with 1cm gap between. Lay a 6cm strip of scrim reinforcement over the card at the spine. Place inside cover over scrim and card cover and glue inside cover to scrim and card cover. Lastly put paper pages of book on top. Sew all pieces together.

Inside cover

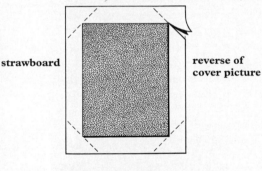

cut along these lines

fold and stick edges onto back of strawboard

strawboard

reverse of cover picture

Repeat for back cover

Outside cover

leave 1cm space between covers

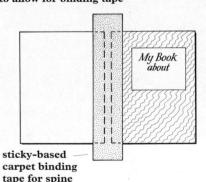

My Book about

Back

Front

place centre of cover design slightly to right to allow for binding tape

My Book about

sticky-based carpet binding tape for spine

Inside pages

fold over and glue down

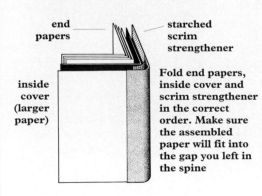

end papers

starched scrim strengthener

inside cover (larger paper)

Fold end papers, inside cover and scrim strengthener in the correct order. Make sure the assembled paper will fit into the gap you left in the spine

scrim glued with PVA

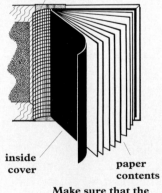

inside cover

paper contents

Make sure that the paper contents is smaller than the cover

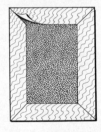

linen thread

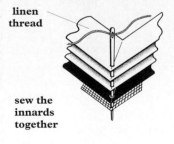

sew the innards together

EVALUATING

Clearly any description or discussion on what has been seen, planned and made in relation to the historic environment constitutes evaluation. Equally, describing to others likes and dislikes, observations or reflections on the products of design and technology, involves pupils in justification, appreciation and review which are a necessary part of the technological process.

Many sites can be used to provoke discussion on the economic, moral, social and environmental implications of the products of design and technology.

THINKING FOR YOURSELF

Use a table like the one below to help focus pupils' evaluation of what they have seen.

Individuals may like to compose their own evaluation of a single object, environment or system and share it with the rest of a class or group. Their summary might include the justification of their own likes and dislikes and proposals for improvement or further development. In evaluating their work, rather than that of past technologists, pupils will increasingly be expected to demonstrate where their knowledge and ideas have come from and how their minds have worked on the problem in hand.

A careful look at one section of this roof will allow your pupils to suggest in pictures how it was constructed. It will influence their construction ideas.

A powerful family commissioned the best design and technologies of the day.

EVALUATION SHEET

Subject						
	Materials	Function	Design	Decoration	Joins	Likes/dislikes
circle the appropriate words	wood	domestic	suits function	plain	none	liked
	stone	military	good	fussy	glue	disliked
	glass	church	bad	minimal	nails/screws	don't know
	concrete	decorative	practical	symmetrical	wooden pegs	beautiful
	brick	furniture	simple	moulded	welding	functional
	plastic	recreation	complicated	handmade	mortar	useful
	metal	industry		carved	other (name)	decorative
	other (name)			other (name)		ugly
						other (name)

Pupils tested their actions against a checklist to evaluate their use of appropriate materials and how well it met its intended purpose.

ASKING OTHERS

Historic environments are often still work places. Custodians, wardens, cleaners, maintenance staff – even office workers and school children work in historic environments. Evaluation can also involve asking the users of such spaces what they feel about them and how they might improve them. Those who are very familiar with historic environments can instantly tell you of the problems they face and the modifications they think necessary.

Use the following ideas to help your pupils decide what to ask and to whom:

■ ask a museum custodian what their favourite and least favourite objects in the collection are and why

■ ask a pupil from another school about the disadvantages and advantages of working in an old building

■ find out from a gardener at a park or country house garden how they think the gardens could be improved

■ listen to the site custodian as he or she tells you about what they do each day

■ ask a restorer or maintenance worker what they think the chief priorities should be in the building or museum

■ choose a cleaner from school

and ask what are the most difficult parts of the building to keep clean and which parts pupils treat most carefully

■ ask a caretaker what their building is like at night and which areas they like the least.

TESTING

If your pupils have made things as a result of a visit then it may be appropriate to test their ideas against a checklist. Their product should have met a need in some way, be fit for its purpose and have used appropriate resources. By Key Stage 3, pupils need to have taken into account the possible social and economic implications, the cost effectiveness and the suitability for manufacture.

Use the following evaluation table to help test the products of design and technology work done in response to a historic site.

A group assignment like this reconstruction of an abbey building can involve pupils in group evaluation.

A checklist such as this could be filled in first by the pupil and then used for others to make an evaluation of their work. Information from it can be used to help pupils consider modifications and improvements.

EVALUATION QUESTIONS	YES	NO
Do you like it?		
Does it fulfill a need?		
Does it have moving parts?		
Is it well made?		
Is it well finished?		
Is it safe?		
Does it use the right materials?		
Is it going to be expensive?		
Are materials easy to get?		
Is it easy to make again?		
Do you think it will be popular?		
Do you think it will sell?		
Would people from other cultures like it?		
Would anyone be offended by it?		

TECHNOLOGY ACROSS THE CURRICULUM

Teachers are being encouraged to look at links between design and technology and other areas of the curriculum to make learning more effective. While undertaking design and technology projects, pupils are often presented with opportunities to apply knowledge, skills and understanding from other subjects areas.

HISTORY

History is obviously present in every activity in an historic environment. It can be used simply as a starting point, the illustration of a principle or it can be the subject of a design and technology assignment and therefore inform every part of the planning and making process. Double benefit can be gained when the design and technology project is linked with the history programmes of study.

Historical monuments like castles or former grand homes of wealthy owners, allow pupils to investigate how such a place was heated or lighted; what remains of the sanitation provision and how a water supply was maintained. The design and technology of doors and windows could form the focus of a project based at a large house. Pupils can investigate door and window shapes, hinges and catches, how they were bolted and what decorative designs were used. When visiting a prehistoric monument such as standing stones, pupils can address the problem – how did people transport such heavy stones and how did they put them into place?

GEOGRAPHY

With its special interest in maps, plans, environments and directions, geographical skills can be used in the observation and the recording of background information for a technology assignment. For example, when investigating the technological aspects of an industrial site, geographical skills are used when studying the transportation system; the sources of energy used on site; how the product was made; how it was moved about and the location and function of various pieces of machinery.

SCIENCE

Science, especially of forces and materials, provides skills relevant to most design and technology work. When pupils are deciding on the most appropriate material to use in their design, they may have to consider the properties of each material – its appearance, colour,

Portchester Castle, Hampshire.

English Heritage Photo Library/Skyscan Balloon Photography

English Heritage Photo Library

Museum objects can provide a wealth of design and technology inspiration.

The use of pattern in design may involve pupils in mathematical concepts.

Many assignments involve pupils taking accurate measurements.

hardness, absorption of water, reaction to heat and its durability. Investigations into the restoration of a derelict building could involve the identification of the effects of weathering and erosion on building materials or the wear and tear of volumes of people visiting the site. In reconstructing the technology used by those who built stone monuments like Stonehenge, pupils will also explore the scientific principles of forces. This is also true when pupils investigate the use of columns, arches and flying buttresses on churches, cathedrals and abbey sites.

MATHEMATICS

Mathematics in its concentration upon number, shape and computation teach skills relevant to most design and technology work. When surveying a site as part of a technology assignment, pupils will be using standard or non-standard units of measurement to calculate perimeter, area, volume or height; model-making demands some understanding of scale, proportion and shape; and the use of pattern in design may involve symmetry, rotation or tessellation.

ENGLISH

Language and literary targets can be incorporated into any design and technology assignment. The use of the historic environment as a context for an assignment will stimulate pupils to broaden their vocabulary not only in historical terms but also those used in architecture and conservation. Some of the recording work undertaken on site is likely to be written in the form of notes, individual words or the completion of questionnaires. Some may be spoken – the recording of findings onto tape or the questionning of an expert. Working in groups can involve a high level of verbal communication which can be further developed by asking pupils to present their ideas to their peers or to other adults. The re-drafting of reports demands skills in organising information, reviewing and presentation. Pupils can be encouraged to use word processors or desk-top publishing software.

ART

Technological aspects of the historic environment can provide pupils with stimulating opportunities to utilise skills, knowledge and understanding developed in art. The skill of being able to draw from direct experience or to take photographs can allow pupils to create reference images which form the basis of their designs. They can use dry materials such as chalk, pencils and crayons to suggest colours, tones and textures.

RELIGIOUS EDUCATION

In our multi-cultural and multi-faith society, it is now possible in many areas to view building technologies which have their roots in quite distant civilizations. Synagogues, temples, mosques and prayer rooms of other religions and cultures are frequently happy to allow pre-booked classes access to places of worship if they can be assured of due reverence and respect.

MUSIC AND PHYSICAL EDUCATION

Movement and mass can be effectively expressed and often more deeply understood when linked with music or physical education. The concepts of force, balance and counter balance can be taught more effectively by using physical group work in PE lessons. For example, dance and movement assignments involving bridges or castle drawbridges can explore the idea of balance and counterbalance as exhibited by a cantilever mechanism.

CITIZENSHIP

Thinking and talking about the environmental impact of everything from a manhole cover to a cathedral is central to the fostering of a concern for the environment. Visits to the historic environment of any period are a practical and realistic way to teach environmental awareness. Citizenship education should aim at producing conservation conscious citizens with an appreciation of the importance of sustainable development. Perhaps the environmental pollution of a badly designed car park or shopping complex could be seen as detrimental to the everyday lives of ordinary people today as atmospheric pollution was in the last century.

OTHER CULTURES

Without the necessity of world travel it is still easily possible to apprehend design and technology from other cultures both now and in the past. Most local museums have inherited disparate collections of objects from other countries and whilst many are not on display curators are increasingly happy to bring out items given good notice. The large national collections at the Victoria and Albert Museum and the British Museum are world famous and special trips to London ought not to be dismissed especially if their focus is multicultural.

Design and technology from other cultures can be particularly stimulating to modern designers because of the different viewpoints and materials which have influenced their production. Take for example musical instruments from the collection at the Horniman Museum – the use of gourds, ivory, animal skins and light soft woods are in great contrast to the more familiar western musical instruments yet their sounds are just as exciting and loud.

It is important that any educational contact with non European cultures has the aim of building respect and understanding. We owe the designers and builders of Africa, Asia and the Americas a great deal. The irrigation and building

technologies of the Arab countries predate the development of similar systems in Europe by centuries. Navigational aids and mapping skills were developed in non European societies well before our own. 'Gothic' pointed arches were actually predated by several centuries by those in Syria and other parts of the Muslim world. Indeed Muslims ensured the survival of Classical learning in science, medicine and technology during the early medieval period in Europe. Pupils may need reminding of such key contributions to our own historic environment before they look at more modern contributions from other traditions.

Some of the following ideas may help focus on our heritage from other cultures:

■ use a visit to a local mosque or temple to make comparison between the ceremonies of Muslims and Christians and how their buildings reflect these differences. Look also at the modes of decoration, orientation of buildings and provision for worshippers

■ be sure to include people of other ethnic backgrounds in all questionnaires. Their perspective on British historic buildings is a valuable reflection on the diversity of modern British Society

■ collect illustrations of the traditional clothing styles of other cultures. Use it to help describe differences and similarities. Explain the relationship between design and culture or religion using clothes as an example

■ make a special study of how kingship or leadership is expressed in clothes or royal artefacts like thrones, crowns and sceptres. Design and make your own crown which combines some of the symbols you have noticed

■ find out how cultures of the past and present deal with death. Look at Roman cremations, Egyptian mummies or the funeral goods of other cultures. Then go on to design an original memorial for yourself.

Architectural features of religious buildings can form the focus of assignments.

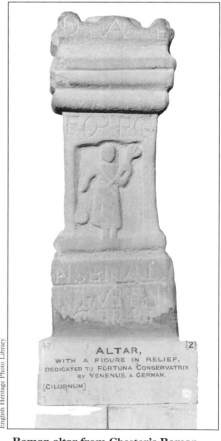

Roman altar from Chester's Roman Fort, Hadrian's Wall.

ILLUSTRATED GLOSSARY

BUILDING MATERIALS

Windows

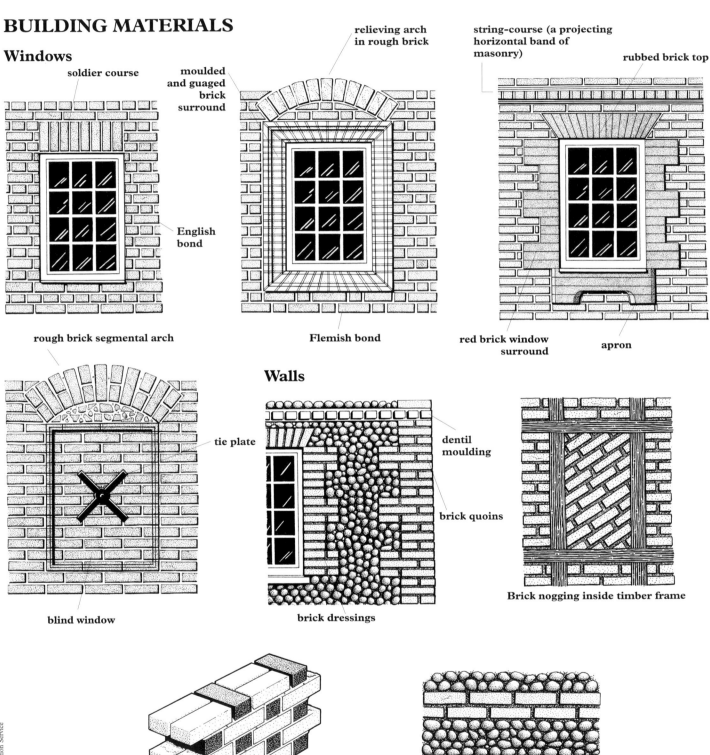

soldier course

relieving arch in rough brick

string-course (a projecting horizontal band of masonry)

rubbed brick top

moulded and guaged brick surround

English bond

rough brick segmental arch

Flemish bond

red brick window surround

apron

Walls

tie plate

dentil moulding

brick quoins

blind window

brick dressings

Brick nogging inside timber frame

Flemish bond wall, stretcher, header, chequered blue and red bricks

Brick and flint lacing course

Walls

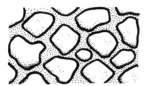

Compact irregular

Irregular rubble

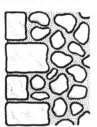

Galletting using small slivers of stone

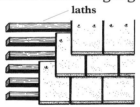

Quoins – squared stones used to finish the corner of a building

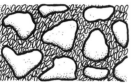

Brick quoins with flint

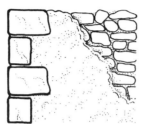

Lime and sand rendering

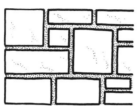

'Snecked' coursing – regular coursing with interruptions

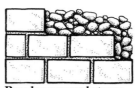

Regular squared stones called ashlar covering wall rubble

Unknapped herringbone

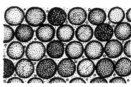

Knapped flint

Square knapped flint

Chequer-board flint with limestone or sandstone

Flint galletting

Flint cobbles

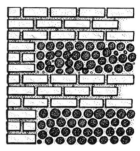

Flint and brick horizontal lacing

Roof and hanging tiles

laths

Plain tiles

Shaped tiles

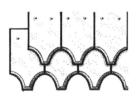

Mathematical tiles

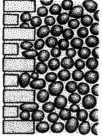

Hanging tile

Stucco plaster over rough brick

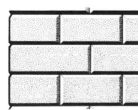

Rustication – artifically weathered joints between stones often made in plaster

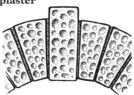

Vermiculated rustication

Bonds

No bond

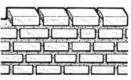

English bond

Flemish bond

Header bond

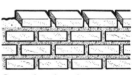

Stretcher bond

Chequer-board with blue bricks

Moulded brick

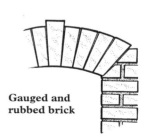

Gauged and rubbed brick

33

ARCHES

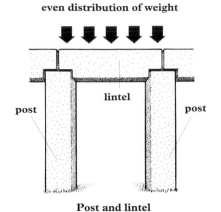

even distribution of weight

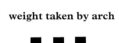

post — lintel — post

Post and lintel

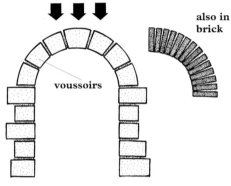

weight taken by arch

voussoirs

also in brick

Semi-circular Romanesque arch

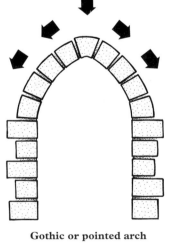

weight is distributed to upright supports

Gothic or pointed arch

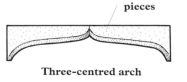

can be made in two pieces

Three-centred arch

COLUMNS

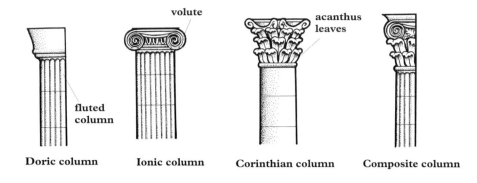

volute

acanthus leaves

fluted column

Doric column   **Ionic column**   **Corinthian column**   **Composite column**

BUTTRESSES

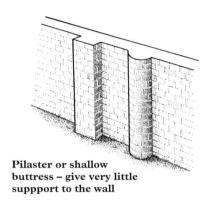

Pilaster or shallow buttress – give very little suppport to the wall

Triangular buttress

Stepped buttress – gives very strong support

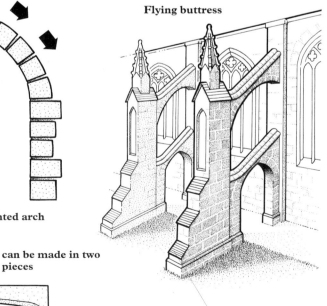

Flying buttress

battered base

weight is carried downwards

English Heritage Education Service

BIBLIOGRAPHY AND RESOURCES

Books

Alderton, D, *Using industrial sites*, English Heritage, 1995
ISBN 1-85074-445-9

Allen, S, Hollinshead, E & Wilkinson, S, *Using houses and homes*, English Heritage, 1998
ISBN 1-85074-398-3

Black, M, *Food & cooking in nineteenth-century Britain*, English Heritage, 1985 ISBN 1-85074-539-0

Black, M, *Food & cooking in medieval Britain*, English Heritage, 1985 ISBN 1-85074-535-8

Brears, P, *Food & cooking in sixteenth-century Britain*, English Heritage, 1985 ISBN 1-85074-536-6

Copeland, T, *Maths and the historic environment*, English Heritage, 1992 ISBN 1-85074-329-0

Copeland, T, *Geography and the historic environment*, English Heritage, 1993 ISBN 1-85074-332-0

Corbishley, G, *Appetite for change – food and cooking in twentieth-century Britain*, English Heritage, 1993 ISBN 1-85074-400-9

Davies, I & Webb, C, *Using documents*, English Heritage, 1996
ISBN 1-85074-478-5

Durbin, G, Morris, S & Wilkinson, S, *Learning from objects*, English Heritage, 1990
ISBN 1-85074-259-6

Keen, J, *Ancient Technology*, English Heritage, 1996
ISBN 1-85074-448-3

Keith, C, *Using listed buildings*, English Heritage, 1991
ISBN 1-85074-297-9

Lockey, M & Walmsley, D, *Art and the historic environment*, English Heritage, 1999
ISBN 1-85074-651-6

McAleavy, T, *Life in a medieval castle*, English Heritage, 1998
ISBN 1-85074-665-6

McAleavy, T, *Life in a medieval abbey*, English Heritage, 1996
ISBN 1-85074-592-7

Macaulay, D, *Castle*, Collins, 1988
ISBN 0-00-192158-4

Morris, R & Corbishley, M, *Churches, cathedrals and chapels*, English Heritage, 1996
ISBN 1-85074-447-5

Pownell, J & Hutson, N, *Science and the historic environment*, English Heritage, 1992
ISBN 1-85074-331-2

Primary History – Using the evidence of the historic environment, English Heritage, 1999
ISBN 1-85074-650-8

Purkis, Sallie, *Using school buildings*, English Heritage, 1993
ISBN 1-85074-379-7

Renfrew, J, *Food & cooking in Roman Britain*, English Heritage, 1985 ISBN 1-85074-534-X

Posters

English Parish Church, English Heritage, 1995

Looking at castles poster pack, English Heritage, 1994 ISBN 1-85074-490-4

Roman Britain poster pack, English Heritage,1997 ISBN 1-85074-692-3

Videos

English Heritage videos are available for free loan or for purchase through mail order.

According to the evidence, English Heritage, 1998, 30 minutes. Suitable for Key Stage 2 and

The investigation of ribbed vaulting can introduce pupils to past technological solutions to forces and weight distribution.

David Walmsley

Jonathan Barnes

Ceramic dish inspired by the investigation of Romanesque designs from Ely Cathedral.

in-service training. It presents a variety of sources, from museum objects and historic sites to archives and artists' impressions, presenting evidence about places, people and events in the past from different points of view.

Building an abbey – Medieval technology at Rievaulx abbey, English Heritage, 1988, 14 minutes. Suitable for key stages 2 and 3.

Historic site – a sculptor's view, English Heritage, 1991, 23 minutes. Suggests applications of ideas for art, design and technology which teachers can develop using any historic site.

How parish churches evolved, English Heritage, 1997, 21 minutes. This explores the developing architectural styles of parish churches over the last 1,400 years.

Master builders – the construction of a great church, English Heritage, 1991, 23 minutes. Medieval technology, engineering and design methods are explored using the building of Beverley Minster cathedral.

Stonehenge – a journey back in time, Cromwell Films & English Heritage, 1998, 30 minutes. This video brings vividly to life how Stonehenge was built; where the building materials came from; how they have been transported and the technology involved in its construction.

Stott Park Bobbin Mill – how a bobbin was made, English Heritage, 1993, 15 minutes. Suitable for key stages 2 and 3.

Acknowledgements

I would like to thank Stirling Clark for many of the ideas which form the core of this book. In addition Danny Rikh, Andy Willmoth and Paul Shallcross for reading and commenting so helpfully on the text.

Our Education Service aims to help teachers at all levels make best use of the resource of the historic environment. Educational groups can make free visits to over 400 historic properties in the care of English Heritage. The following booklets are free on request. **Visiting Historic Sites** contains a full list of all our sites, details of how to book a visit, and activities for National Curriculum work on site. Our magazine, **Heritage Learning**, is published three times a year. **Resources**, our catalogue, lists all our educational books, videos, posters and slide packs. Please contact:

**English Heritage
Education Service
FREEPOST 22 (WD214)
London WlE 7EZ
Tel: 020 7973 3442
Fax: 020 7973 3443
http:/www.english-heritage.
org.uk**